This Book Belongs to

MANY THANKS to the TALENTED elves
IN OUR NORTH WALES WORKSHOP
FOR PUTTING THIS "CHRISTMAS COMPANION" TOGETHER...

...JENNIFER, KATIE, MARJORIE...AND JODI...

❊

...ON DASHER, ON DANCER.....

❊

ISBN 0-7683-2279-0

Compiled and illustrated by Kathy Davis

© 2000 Kathy Davis Designs
www.kathydavis.com
All Rights Reserved

Published in 2000 by Cedco Publishing Company.
100 Pelican Way, San Rafael, California 94901
For a free catalog of other Cedco® products, please write
to the address above, or visit our website : www.cedco.com

Printed in Hong Kong

1 3 5 7 9 10 8 6 4 2

CHRISTMAS COMPANION

A RECORD BOOK OF HOLIDAY MEMORIES & TRADITIONS

Cedco Publishing Company . San Rafael, California

INTRODUCTION

YOUR "CHRISTMAS COMPANION" WILL PROVIDE YOU WITH
MANY YEARS OF ENJOYMENT, CAPTURING TEN YEARS
WORTH OF HOLIDAY MEMORIES AND TRADITIONS IN A
TREASURY THAT IS SURE TO BECOME A FAMILY HEIRLOOM.

*

THE "CHRISTMAS COMPANION" IS DIVIDED INTO TWO PARTS,
CHRISTMAS MEMORIES & CHRISTMAS TRADITIONS.

CHRISTMAS MEMORIES

THIS SECTION PROVIDES PAGES TO PLACE PHOTOS, CHRISTMAS CARDS,
AND JOURNALED REFLECTIONS OF THE HOLIDAY - AS WELL AS
HIGHLIGHTS OF EACH YEAR. THERE IS A SPOT FOR YOUR FAMILY
CHRISTMAS CARD, HOWEVER, YOU MAY CHOOSE INSTEAD TO USE
THIS SPACE TO ATTACH A FAVORITE CARD OR LETTER RECEIVED,
OR POSSIBLY MORE PHOTOS. BLANK PAGES MAY BE FILLED WITH
ADDITIONAL OVERFLOW OF PHOTOS AND NOTES.

Christmas Traditions

As your family carries on traditions handed down from the past while developing new traditions of their own, you'll want to record the things that make your holiday seasons so special. Plans and preparations, family favorites, gift ideas, decorations, menu and party plans and recipes are all traditions you can save for future reference. Please adapt your "Christmas Companion" to fit your needs,

and most importantly,

have fun using it !!!

May this book become a treasured companion for you through many memorable holiday seasons.

love and joy,

Kathy Davis

IT IS GOOD to BE CHILDREN
SOMETIMES,
AND NEVER BETTER THAN AT CHRISTMAS.
.CHARLES DICKENS.
*

THIS BOOK IS DEDICATED TO THE CHILD IN ALL OF US.

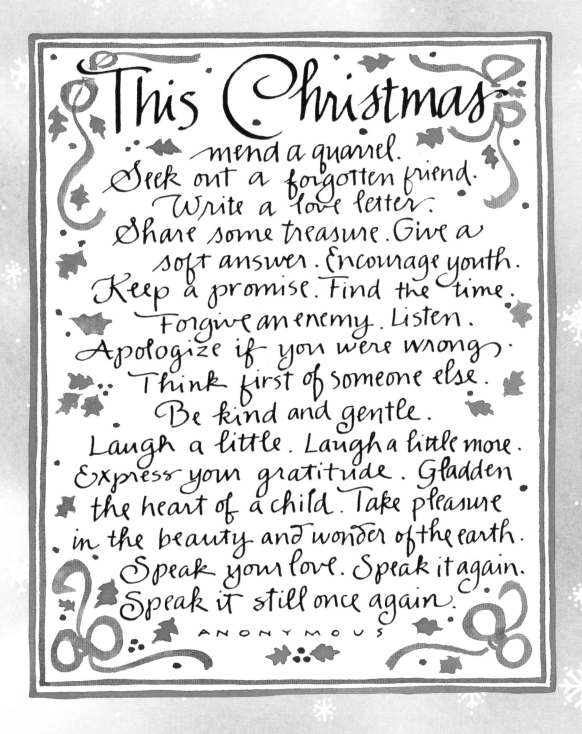

This Christmas

mend a quarrel.
Seek out a forgotten friend.
Write a love letter.
Share some treasure. Give a
soft answer. Encourage youth.
Keep a promise. Find the time.
Forgive an enemy. Listen.
Apologize if you were wrong.
Think first of someone else.
Be kind and gentle.
Laugh a little. Laugh a little more.
Express your gratitude. Gladden
the heart of a child. Take pleasure
in the beauty and wonder of the earth.
Speak your love. Speak it again.
Speak it still once again.

ANONYMOUS

CHRISTMAS MEMORIES

Photos

CHRISTMAS MEMORIES

_____ YEAR

THiS CHRiSTMAS WAS SPECiAL BECAUSE...

FAMiLY AND FRiENDS

FAVORiTE GiFTS

FUN TiMES

REMEMBRANCE, LiKE A CANDLE, SHiNES BRiGHTEST AT CHRiSTMASTiME.

OUR CHRISTMAS Card

HiGHLiGHTS of the YEAR

HOPES for the COMING YEAR

THat which is Loved is always Beautiful · Norwegian proverb.

Greetings of the Season

Olive Branch	Poinsettia	Pine
· PEACE ·	· MIRTH ·	· ENDURANCE ·
Carnation	Winter Greens	Rose
· JOY ·	· HARMONY ·	· LOVE ·
Holly	Mum	Ivy
· FORESIGHT ·	· HOPE ·	· FRIENDSHIP ·

Photos

CHRISTMAS MEMORIES

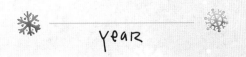

_____ YEAR

THIS CHRISTMAS WAS SPECIAL BECAUSE...

FAMILY AND FRIENDS

FAVORITE GIFTS

FUN TIMES

REMEMBRANCE, LIKE A CANDLE, SHINES BRIGHTEST AT CHRISTMASTIME.

OUR CHRISTMAS Card

HIGHLIGHTS of the YEAR

HOPES FOR the COMING YEAR

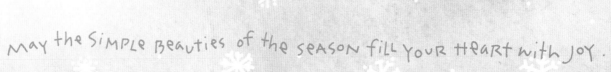

MAY the SIMPLE BEAUTIES of the SEASON fill YOUR HEART with JOY.

Photos

CHRISTMAS MEMORIES

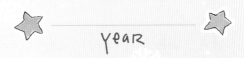

YEAR

THIS CHRISTMAS WAS SPECIAL BECAUSE...

FAMILY AND FRIENDS

FAVORITE GIFTS

FUN TIMES

REMEMBRANCE, LIKE A CANDLE, SHINES BRIGHTEST AT CHRISTMASTIME.

OUR CHRISTMAS Card

HIGHLIGHTS of the YEAR

HOPES for the COMING YEAR

IN a full heart there is ROOM FOR everything, AND IN AN EMPTY HEART THERE is ROOM FOR NOTHING. Antonio Porchia

Photos

CHRISTMAS MEMORIES

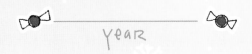
Year

THIS CHRISTMAS WAS SPECIAL BECAUSE...

FAMILY AND FRIENDS

FAVORITE GIFTS

FUN TIMES

REMEMBRANCE, LIKE A CANDLE, SHINES BRIGHTEST AT CHRISTMASTIME.

OUR CHRISTMAS Card

HIGHLIGHTS of the YEAR

HOPES for the COMING YEAR

RICH are THEY WHO TREASURE SIMPLE JOYS.

unknown.

'Tis the
GIFT
To be simple
'Tis the
GIFT
To be free

· SHAKER HYMN ·

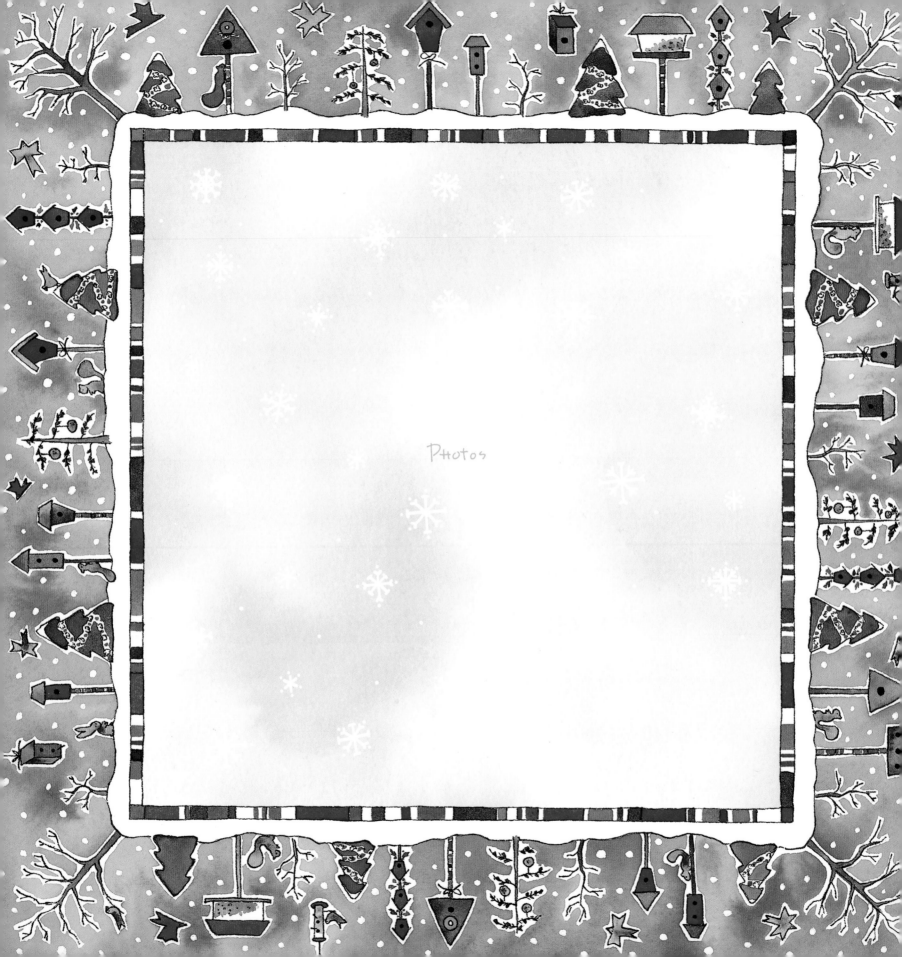

Photos

CHRISTMAS MEMORIES

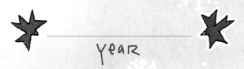

Year

THIS CHRISTMAS WAS SPECIAL BECAUSE...

FAMILY AND FRIENDS

FAVORITE GIFTS

FUN TIMES

REMEMBRANCE, LIKE A CANDLE, SHINES BRIGHTEST AT CHRISTMASTIME.

OUR CHRISTMAS Card

HIGHLIGHTS of the YEAR

HOPES for the COMING YEAR

THE LOVE WE GIVE AWAY IS THE ONLY LOVE WE KEEP · Elbert Hubbard.

No act of Love, however small, is ever wasted.

Aesop

Photos

Christmas Memories

_____ Year

THIS CHRISTMAS WAS SPECIAL BECAUSE...

FAMILY AND FRIENDS

FAVORITE GIFTS

FUN TIMES

REMEMBRANCE, LIKE A CANDLE, SHINES BRIGHTEST AT CHRISTMASTIME.

Our Christmas Card

HIGHLIGHTS of the YEAR

HOPES for the COMING YEAR

Take joy Home and make a place in thy Heart for Her. - Socrates

May you Always have a place in your Heart for the Joy that is Christmas

Photos

CHRISTMAS MEMORIES

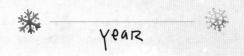

_____ year

THIS CHRISTMAS WAS SPECIAL BECAUSE...

FAMILY AND FRIENDS

FAVORITE GIFTS

FUN TIMES

REMEMBRANCE, LIKE A CANDLE, SHINES BRIGHTEST AT CHRISTMASTIME.

OUR CHRISTMAS Card

HiGHLiGHts of the YEAR

HoPes for the COMiNG YeAR

HeAveN GiVe you MANY, MANY MerrY DAYS · shakespeare

Photos

CHRISTMAS MEMORIES

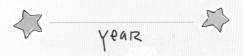

YEAR

THIS CHRISTMAS WAS SPECIAL BECAUSE...

FAMILY AND FRIENDS

FAVORITE GIFTS

FUN TIMES

REMEMBRANCE, LIKE A CANDLE, SHINES BRIGHTEST AT CHRISTMASTIME.

OUR CHRISTMAS Card

HIGHLIGHTS of the YEAR

HOPes for the COMING Year

I WILL HONOR CHRISTMAS IN MY HEART and TRY to keep it all the YEAR.
.CHARLES DICKENS.

Photos

CHRISTMAS MEMORIES

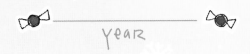

Year

THIS CHRISTMAS WAS SPECIAL BECAUSE...

FAMILY AND FRIENDS

FAVORITE GIFTS

FUN TIMES

· REMEMBRANCE, LIKE A CANDLE, SHINES BRIGHTEST AT CHRISTMASTIME·

OUR CHRISTMAS Card

HIGHLIGHTS of the YEAR _____

_____

_____

_____

_____

_____

_____

_____

HOPES FOR the COMING YEAR _____

_____

_____

_____

_____

ALL the LOVE we come to KNOW in LIFE
COMES FROM the LOVE we KNEW as CHILDREN.
·unknown·

It is good to be

CHILDREN

sometimes,

...and never better

than at

CHRISTMAS

CHARLES DICKENS

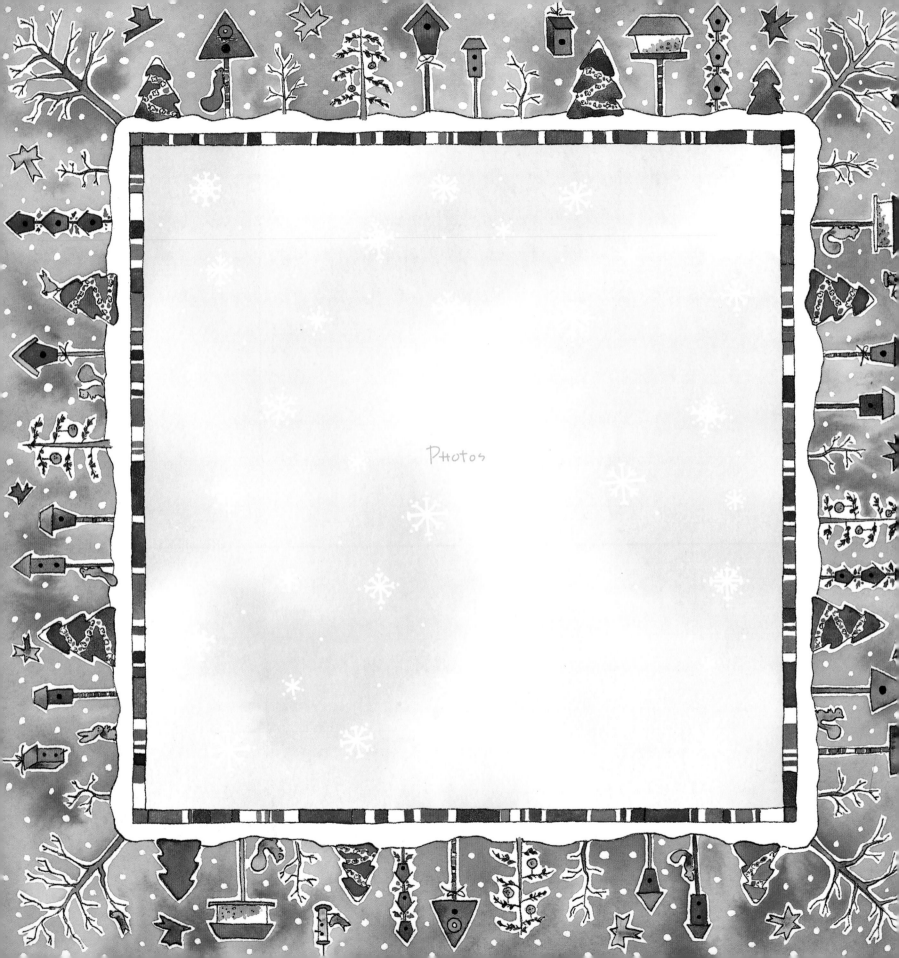

Photos

CHRISTMAS MEMORIES
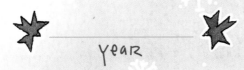
Year

THIS CHRISTMAS WAS SPECIAL BECAUSE...

FAMILY AND FRIENDS

FAVORITE GIFTS

FUN TIMES

REMEMBRANCE, LIKE A CANDLE, SHINES BRIGHTEST AT CHRISTMASTIME.

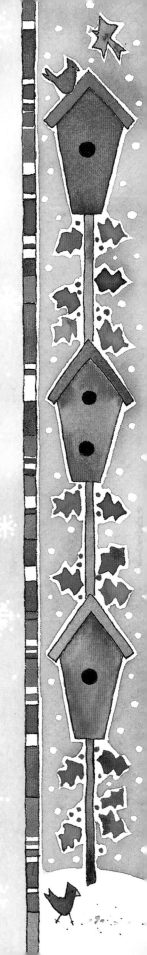

OUR CHRISTMAS Card

HiGHLiGHts of the YeaR

Hopes for the Coming YeaR

make a joyful noise! Psalms 66:1.

THE YEARS TEACH US MUCH WHICH the DAYS NEVER KNEW - Ralph Waldo Emerson

Christmas Traditions

Countdown to Christmas

Preparations and Anticipations

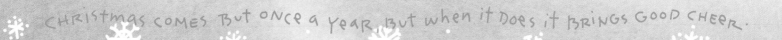
CHRISTMAS COMES BUT ONCE A YEAR, BUT WHEN IT DOES IT BRINGS GOOD CHEER.

Countdown to Christmas

one month before...

Three weeks Before...

one thing today . another tomorrow . one thing today . another tomorrow .

Countdown to Christmas

Two weeks before...

one week before...

TIME IS NATURE'S way of KEEPING everything FROM HAPPENING at once. unknown

Countdown to Christmas

CHRISTMAS eve

CHRISTMAS DAY

'TIS the SEASON ... TO Be BUSY !!!

THE MOST wasted of Days is that in which one has Not LAUGHed. Sebastian Chamfort

family favorites
special things we do each year

religious celebrations

pageants · plays · performances

treat your friends like family and your family like friends · cotton mather

family favorites

special things we do each year

CONCERTS

places we visit

shopping excursions

we Gathered, we feasted, we'll never forget

family favorites

FAVORITE MOVIES

Favorite T.V. Specials

Favorite Cookies and Confections

Favorite Ornaments

TOGETHER is the Nicest place to be · SHARED joy is DOUBLE joy .

family favorites

Favorite stories

Favorite games

Favorite quiet times

EVEN WHEN YOU'RE FAR AWAY, HOME IS WHERE YOUR HEART WILL STAY.

Gift *ideas*

People We Need to Remember

CHRISTMAS WON'T BE CHRISTMAS WITHOUT ANY PRESENTS. Louisa May Alcott.

Gift ideas

Gifts from the kitchen

Handmade Gift ideas

The most meaningful gifts are those tied with heartstrings.

Gift Ideas

Gifts from the HEART

Gifts to those less fortunate

IT IS IN GIVING THAT WE RECEIVE. St Francis of Assisi

THE MiRacLe of CHRISTMas is the Gift of Love.

Gift ideas

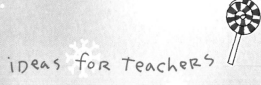

ideas for teachers

ideas for special helpers

creative gift wrap ideas

WE MUST NOT ONLY GIVE WHAT WE HAVE, WE MUST ALSO GIVE WHAT WE ARE
.Desiree. Joseph Mercier.

Decorations

IDEAS FOR OUTDOORS

IDEAS FOR INDOORS

COLLECTIONS

DECK THE HALLS WITH BOUGHS OF HOLLY... FA LA LA LA LA, LA LA LA LA.

Decorations

Tree ideas

Ornaments

Crafts to make

'Tis the season to be jolly, fa la la la la, la la la la.

Party and Menu Plans

CELEBRATIONS HAVE TO BE MADE, TROUBLES COME BY THEMSELVES. Yiddish Proverb.

PARTY and MENÜ PLANS

TOO MUCH OF A GOOD THING CAN BE WONDERFUL !!! - Mae West

Recipes

Recipe for: _____

From: _____   Serves: _____

_____
_____
_____
_____
_____
_____
_____
_____
_____

Recipe for: _____

From: _____   Serves: _____

_____
_____
_____
_____
_____
_____
_____
_____
_____

FROM SOUP to NUTS · FOOD, GLORIOUS FOOD · eat, DRINK and Be MERRY

Recipes

Recipe for:

From: Serves:

Recipe for:

From: Serves:

THERE IS NO LOVE SINCERER THAN THE LOVE OF FOOD · George Bernard Shaw

Recipes

Recipe for: _____ From: _____ Serves: _____

_____

_____

_____

_____

_____

_____

_____

_____

_____

_____

_____

_____

_____

_____

_____

Little Jack Horner sat in a corner, eating a Christmas pie

Recipes

Recipe for: From: Serves:

_____

_____

_____

_____

_____

Recipe for: From: Serves:

_____

_____

_____

_____

_____

He PUT IN HiS THUMB AND PULLed out a PLUM and said "What a good boy am I!"
- Nursery rhyme.

MeRRY CHRiStMas to all AND to all a GOOD NiGHt !

OTHER BOOKS BY KATHY DAVIS
AND CEDCO PUBLISHING:

✳ "FRIENDS ARE FLOWERS THAT NEVER FADE"
   GIFT BOOK AND MATCHING JOURNAL
✳ "THE TIME TO BE HAPPY IS NOW"
   A BOOK OF INSPIRATIONS
   AND MATCHING ADDRESS BOOK

FOR OTHER KATHY DAVIS PRODUCT:

✳ VISIT THE ORIGINAL KATHY DAVIS RETAIL STORE,
   LOCATED IN NORTH WALES, PA.
   CALL 215·661·8444 FOR INFO

✳ VISIT OUR ONLINE STORE AT
   WWW.KATHYDAVIS.COM
   OR CALL 1·877·542·2797 FOR A FREE CATALOG

✳ ASK A RETAILER NEAR YOU!

Kathy Davis
COLLECTION

A PORTION OF THE PROCEEDS
FROM THE SALE OF THIS BOOK
HELPS THE HOMELESS THROUGH THE
NATIONAL INTERFAITH HOSPITALITY NETWORK

KathyDavis

Has always loved art.
a former teacher, she designed
her new career one greeting card at a time.
her colorful style and uplifting messages now adorn
thousands of products found worldwide. Kathy is widely
recognized for her popular Christmas cards, which showcase
a broad range of illustration styles. from soft watercolors
to bold graphics, her work is known for its inspiring verse
and warmhearted whimsy. Kathy lives in the philadelphia area
with her family and a menagerie of pets.